A
REGIMENTAL MESS

by

First published 1993

Published by Owl Press. PO Box 315 Downton, Salisbury, Wiltshire. SP5 3YE
Printed and bound in Great Britain by Redwood Books Ltd Trowbridge, Wiltshire.
Origination and design by Owl Press

British Library Cataloguing-in-Publication Data. A catalogue record for this book is available from the British Library.
ISBN 0 9515917 5 4

OWL PRESS are donating a royalty from the sale of this book to support the work of SSAFA, the Soldiers', Sailors' and Airmen's Families Association.

FOREWORD
by General Sir Peter de la Billière

The ability of the British soldier to laugh despite his, and increasingly her, difficulties during times of adversity in war and peace is renowned and respected; it was always a weathervane of his morale.

During the last century the size of the Army has fluctuated according to the perceived need of the hour. After fighting a Cold War for 45 years, and winning, there are new challenges ahead for those who are due to leave and those who will be able to stay in our Army. All will be affected in some way but throughout, the soldier's sense of humour will soften the sharp edge of disbandment, amalgamation and redundancy in the same way as it alleviates the cruelties of conflict whether in general war or on the streets of Belfast.

The cartoonist who has created this book suffered an earlier bout of Options for Change when his regiment, the Loyals, became part of the Queen's Lancashire Regiment. His great sense of fun coupled with his loyalty to Queen, country and pride in being a British soldier make this book a treasure to enjoy.

When all the dust has settled and we have forged new traditions from the old, "A Regimental Mess" will be there for us all to laugh about these turbulent days of the early 1990's.

Peter de la Billière

Other titles by OWL PRESS
Military and Humour Specialists

Gumboots and Pearls. The life of a wife of....*by Annie Jones*
The Backstabber's Guide *ed. by Annie Jones, politics by Austin Mitchell MP*
Bullets and Bandsmen. The story of a bandsman on the Western Front *by Daphne Jones*
David, We're Pregnant! *101 cartoons by Lynn Johnston*
Hi Mum! Hi Dad! The first year of parenthood. *101 cartoons by Lynn Johnston*
Do They Ever Grow Up? The terrible twos and beyond. *101 cartoons by Lynn Johnston*

About The Author

David Downe

David Downe was born, chuckling, during the depression of 1931 and is still smiling during the current depresion. In between times he was educated at St Edwards Oxford and the Royal Military Academy Sandhurst. He was commissioned into the 47th Foot (the Loyal Regiment NL) in 1951, provided with an 'option for change' in 1968 and became variously thereafter, unemployed for one blissful year, a freelance cartoonist in Fleet Street and ultimately Director of the West Midlands Area Museum Service. After living like a gypsy with no caravan, he and his family have settled into civilian life near Worcester.

During his career as a cartoonist he has contributed to the cartoon columns of most of the popular and less popular press as well as to specialist collections. His own books include "Isandlhwana and All That" and "Downe On His Luck". A member of the Cartoonist Club of Great Britain, David is presently engaged as a Trustee of the Army Museums Ogilby Trust and the Dyson Perrins Worcester Porcelain Museum Trust, where he does more than doodle.

To Wendy

THE CAST ON PARADE

Major Barbour, 'Splodge' to his friends.

Lance Corporal Justin Vest GBH.

Major Rupert Barbour MBE

As far back as he could remember, Rupert always knew he was going to have a career in the Army. His father and his grandfather before him had been Colonels of the Regiment (pronounced wegiment.) It had always been a jolly good jape, rather like being at prep school only he went home to Daphne instead of matron. Although when he thought of it, there often wasn't much difference... he still got a stiff telling off for wearing his riding boots in the sitting room.

Rupert had never thought of any other career. Whenever he met civilians, which, he had to confess was not very often these days, he was always amazed at how they worked. They didn't have Wednesday and Friday afternoons off but always finished work at the same time whatever else was happening in the world. He really couldn't see himself wearing civvies let alone working with them. And commuting!!..... that was the ultimate dirty word to someone who had always walked to work. Where would he leave the dogs if they couldn't come to the office with him? Becoming a Civvy was an unbearable thought. So when the letter came round asking for volunteers to take redundancy, he ceremoniously threw it towards the bin. For the fourth time that morning he missed. 'Damn,' he thought as he strolled over to pick up the crumpled ball of paper, 'It's no wonder I never made it into the Regiment's basketball team.'

Entering overalls for the final dinner night.

"My God! - Radio One"

"Who's responsible for this monumental mess?"

"Perhaps I might be a market gardener -
perhaps..!"

"I AM going to be a captain of industry - I am
GOING to be..."

Daphne Barbour

Like many a true officer's wife Daphne has long since abandoned any thought of living in the twentieth century. She is untainted by modern consumerism. Her values, like her pearls and table linen, go back a long way. It is far more important to her to have Frank Cooper's marmalade sent over regularly from home than buy a new Barbour and wellies. When she goes out, to walk their two labradors, she throws on her battered old Barbour, pulls down the oilskin hat and tramps off in her wellies. She hasn't the time or inclination to be trendy. After all, if it is good enough for the Queen to look like this, it will certainly do for her.

When she married dear old Rupert she knew it would be her duty to support him. Despite her expensive education she had never had any thought of earning a living. Actually **earning** money was such a bore it was far easier to do without. When Daphne was married she had more than enough to do looking after Rupert and the dogs. He was simply hopeless. She spent nearly every morning turning the house upside down looking for his papers and his keys. Just when she thought he'd left and she'd put the kettle on for another cup of coffee, he'd come bursting in through the front door shouting for his ID card.

Daphne not only considered it her duty but her job to be on nearly every committee in the Garrison. There was the Wives' Club, the Thrift Shop, the SSAFA Committee to name but a few. Together, they were a full time job. She really couldn't see how she could have worked... for money... that is.. let alone have her children home from boarding school. Rupert was married to the Army and she was married to Rupert. It was not only Rupert who was facing redundancy.

"My God darling you need re-shoeing again."

"It's quite incredible how some people treat animals."

"Whose big end?"

"Perhaps we could do a swap?"

Corporal Vest

When he first met his wife Di, Corporal Vest was a hunky young man whose reputation for being tough went with his name. Come wind, snow or rain, when he was in civvies, he wore nothing but jeans, trainers and a vest. It was his trademark. He liked to look hard and thought jumpers were kangaroos. As he'd grown older Corporal Vest had hardly changed. Just a few of the hairs which sprouted like wire wool over the top of his vest had turned grey. And the gap between his vest and his trousers had widened to reveal one fleshy bulge at the front and two at the back.

Corporal Vest would have gone far in the Army if he hadn't been in front of the old man so many times. He'd made Sergeant on at least three occasions. The trouble was he didn't like Civvies.... especially after he'd had a few jars with the lads. Corporal Vest usually managed to pack in a few meaty punches before he was carted off to the slammer. In the morning, with a head that felt it was being compressed by a car crusher he'd be marched in front of the OC (Officer Commanding), which was nothing compared to going home. His fights had gone down in the folklore of the Regiment. They liked a soldier to show good fighting spirit.

He didn't think much about being made redundant. If it happened, it happened. There was not much he could do about it. He had better things to worry about like whether his duty free allowance of booze and cigarettes would last the month or who was captain of the dart's team.

"Three weeks, sixteen hours, twenty-four
minutes, ten seconds to do."

"Good evening Sir."

"Eeee! - you're from 'CIVVIES' on the telly!"

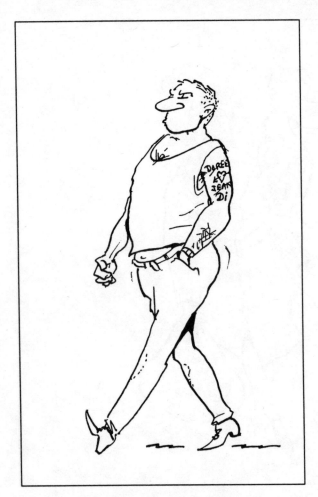

"Civvy Street - here I come!"

"?"

"I am just the sort of forward looking backstabber you seem to be looking for.

I remain, for the moment, your obedient servant Justin Vest .
Lance Corporal Retired."

Desiree (Di) Vest

Di had been married to Corporal Vest for most of her life. They had met when she was fifteen and his Regiment had come into town. In one unforgettable evening at the local disco he had whisked her off her feet.. and a bit more off besides. She loved his muscular body and his colourful tattoos. She listened with rapt attention and believed every word he told her about his dangerous missions in the Army. Overnight he became her hero.

As soon as she turned sixteen they got married and by the time she was thirty-five she looked as if she would be a glamorous granny. She never took much notice of those posh officer's wives who rushed about wearing frilled blouses, pearls and second-hand clothes organising everything. She thought they were snobs but quite liked going to the Wives Club Christmas Disco they organised. They was nothing like it for drinking a bit too much and having a lift home in the duty bus. It was her chance to leave Vesty with a six pack and the babysitting and have a girl's night out.

She lived by her motto, 'They can take me as I am,' and quite often Corporal Vest came home early precisely to do that. He called it his Wednesday afternoon sports. Only he spent the rest of the afternoon doing a bit of Egyptian PT while Di had to nip back to the NAAFI.

"I bet old Vesty thinks I look B....*! great for the Mess tonight."

Di joins Aerobics because she likes the leotard.

Just a few things for the weekend.

THE LEANER MEANER ARMY

Soldiers and their families have always known that re-surfacing of roads or the opening of a new NAAFI spells death for a garrison - but surely Berlin was safe? When Hess died and Spandau prison was levelled to make way for a new NAAFI superstore (instantly renamed Hesco's by the locals), no-one suspected that this innocent event would herald the melting of the Cold War. The Iron Curtain crumbled and left hundreds of miles of mine ridden sand stretched across Europe to become the biggest litter tray in the world for three legged cats.

With no threat from the East it seemed just a bit on the wasteful side to watch billions of pounds of hi-tech military equipment in Germany turn into scrap metal. How much more sensible to move it all back to the UK so that it could rust there. The plan to pull back to our own island and reduce the Forces to a newer, sleeker look was called Options for Change. So now the Forces are over-stocked with men and machines. Every military car park in the UK is becoming full of tanks and equipment.

The men and their families must return to their native shores to join the queues to get into the Job Centres at opening time. Couldn't there have been a better way? Couldn't Salisbury Plain have been turned into a giant Theme Park where adults and children alike could have driven tanks and experienced CS gas? The Army Catering Corps could have stayed alive running fish and chip and spotted dick bars throughout the park. It could have been a great success. We might even have exported our British Army of the Rhine Theme Parks to Europe. There's a well landscaped site available just outside Fallingbostel.

"Look General - just tell them that the decision is maybe and that's final!"

"Meanwhile Ma'am it is our intention that Palace duties will be taken over by the Officer's Pension Society who will be trooping the 'Pennant' next year."

"I wish the Minister would stop saying "It's certainly all go around here."

"The Government has decided on the most economical option gentlemen....all surplus ships, aircraft, stores and equipment will proceed directly to the Bermuda Triangle."

"The Governor's been inundated by applications from ex-service types wanting to defend the pound against the deutschmark."

"Well, I for one will sleep a lot more comfortably."

"What did you do in the Cold War Daddy?"

"He's not a flasher - just flogging bits of the Berlin Wall cheaper than in there."

"So you sold all your uniform and equipment at a car boot sale in Berlin and now you want to come in from the cold?"

"I tell you Igor - we can still make better smells than they can."

"Now you chaps will all realise that these cuts are necessary chiefly because there aren't enough good enemies to go around nowadays."

"I'm sure it won't be anything like that dear."

BLIND DATE

Contrary to expectations Options involves very few options other than staying or leaving. It is much the same as the four standard choices of the old Catering Corps; take it, leave it, like it or lump it. The combining of many regiments bears a closer resemblance to 'Blind Date' than any form of strategic planning. The plan is to lump as many regiments and corps together as possible so that the number of commanding officers, messes, bands and barracks can be reduced to the absolute minimum. Slide rules and calculators flash as the brains at MOD tackle the problem of what to call the new Regiment formed from the 16th/5th Lancers and the 17th/21st Lancers. Will new mascots have to be bred with the head of the goat and the body of an Irish Wolfhound? What A REGIMENTAL MESS!

For the average soldier, Options is just a fancy word for Cuts. After dodging and weaving three waves of redundancy, he can expect little more than back to back tours in Northern Ireland with a three month 'holiday' in Yugoslavia as the only chance of escape. Meanwhile, the staff work day and night to plan the drawdown. They will only be able to say they've finished when they've written themselves out of their jobs.

Whatever the state of confusion you can be sure of one thing: the recruiters will still be promising the world.

"Their mascot was a goat - we hadn't got one so we had to compromise."

"What sort of amalgamation have we got here?"

"Well gentlemen, I hope you have all brought your pocket calculators."

"Perhaps we should refer to it as twinning rather than amalgamation Ma'am?"

"Then after the successful conclusion of my argument with H.M. over the amalgamation of her footguards, I received this unexpected invitation to apply for an appointment at the Tower of London."

"Four tunics. Two with, two without!"

"OK, we've got to reduce to three horsemen of the Apocalypse - War and Pestilence are amalgamated!"

"They didn't have any redundancy or options for change cards."

"She's been amalgamating with some feller at Brigade Headquarters - now he's made her redundant."

GARDENING LEAVE
SUPPLEMENT
NIPPLEWORT (LAPSANA VULGARIS)
MUGWORT (ARTEMISIA)
TANSY (TANACETUM VULGARIS)
CREEPING THISTLE (CARDUUS)

GARDENING LEAVE

The phrase 'Gardening Leave' conjures up ideas of six weeks courses at Wisley or Kew learning the latin name for every kind of vegetation known to man (and woman). For many soldiers a stint of horticultural education would indeed be more use, if less enjoyable, than a period of enforced idleness.

But as some of the old crew, those who can remember the times before overstretch, know, Gardening Leave used to be that coveted time off between postings. A time when a soldier could be most usefully employed propping up the local bars at Her Majesty's expense. Gardening Leave, once so rare and never long enough, is now to be dreaded. In the present state of confusion, it can last anything from 3 to 9 months which is plenty of time for the axe to fall on the next job. It's not that they're not trying their hardest at MOD personel branches but the game has changed from fitting square pegs into round holes to musical chairs. Every time they think they've got enough postings for their men, the Treasury takes a whole lot more away.

The Armed Forces are secretly praying for another war and harping back to the Good Old Days of the Falklands and Gulf Wars. In six months time a tour in a bunker in Northern Ireland may look attractive.

"All this gardening leave is punching one hell of a hole in the ozone layer old man."

"- biggest marrow at the Middle Wallop flower show 1992 Sir."

"Stand by your beds!"

"It's all right dear. Even a proper gardener could have done something like that."

"Why can't you Sappers spread your manure by hand like everyone else?"

"It's quite safe dear, you cut your way in on a bearing of 190 degrees and then find your way back to me on a back bearing of 10 degrees."

"We vacate the forward marrow trenches by 1800 hours and regroup at the potting shed destroying any isolated pockets of slugs on the way."

"- and now for the Regimental slow mulch - the green, green grass of home."

"Frankly, all this gardening leave is knackering me."

"A really nice man in Sainsburys said it was ideal for spreading on rhubarb."

BACK TO BLIGHTY

As drawdown from BAOR draws nearer, soldiers and their families must relinquish their tax free allowances, cheap petrol and overseas allowance and return to their native shores. How happy they must feel to be coming home to TV licenses and Council Tax. The Pickfords vans will be lining the autobahns like wagon trains and the RAF will make sure that it's 'Duty Frees, Women and Children First' as they fill their passenger flights back to UK.

In Germany everyone has caught the selling up fever. There are the 'shranks' that won't shrink and the pets that cost more than a redundancy package to put through quarantine. The second hand market in cars, boats, furniture, cats, dogs, guinea pigs the lot.... is going through the floor. They can't give the stuff away. The NAAFI's in Berlin and elsewhere, are joining in the great sale of the century. Soon there'll be nothing left on the shelves but tins of spam, razor blades and toilet rolls. It's anyone's guess whether they'll re-stock for those staying on.

Coming home is not all it's cracked up to be. Soon soldiers and their families who've been missing mum for a few years will be living with her. After six months waiting for accommodation most soldiers will be glad to take what the MOD has on offer even if it is a bivvi for four plus a goldfish on Salisbury Plain. For those lucky enough to get a house it is bound to be at least four times smaller than their Pickford's van. Once it has been unloaded and the house is visibly bulging, a soldier can begin his hunt for a chip shop that serves bratties and frites.

"No, we are NOT being 'ethnically cleansed' - just posted home!"

"Your pounds are going to float and you will be able to wash your car on Sundays next year."

"You realise that every time you shove hard down there something pops out up here?"

"It's OK luv - apparently there's a 'Little Chef' down the road that does an ALL day bratwurst."

"This is a vegetarian library - we don't stock good meaty novels!"

"And a letter from a Mr Vest saying he's going to march into 50 Kenneth Kaunda Close on July 5th."

"I'm afraid Mrs Barbour, you are not covered for damage incurred during a private airdrop on Salisbury Plain."

"Jumbo boxes for Brigadiers and above are over at Imber Clump."

"He thinks I should get my name down now for the accommodation, free tickets for Wimbledon and the Festival of Remembrance at the Albert Hall."

"OK, I become a Buddhist , you become a nun, we invite your mother to live here, all the children come home - I go mad, and that totally exempts us from paying Council Tax."

"Nothing to do with the Army dear - some Civvy business."

"Sergeant Major Slump seems to be settling down well as a born again b.......d!!"

"A real road hog deterrent, complete with radio, well maintained - AND bloody hard to clamp!"

"How can I possibly work with someone who thinks that REME and SIGS means brandy and cigars?"

"British Army of the Nadder somehow doesn't have the same ring to it."

"Now we're back in UK you must remember to read the small print on our hire purchase agreements."

"It's just like a dinner night darling, without the band and the tight trousers."

"You haven't got a nice middle aged Captain or Sergeant Major for a woman about Size 18?"

STAYING ON

With two-thirds of the British population departed from BAOR there'll no longer be a waiting list for Brownies, schools, hospitals and the like. Army housing areas, once echoing from street to street with the sound of noisy young children and dogs, will become still. Any children staying on will be in danger of being kidnapped from the sweet shop or playground to join Sunday School. Perhaps services will be cut back in line with the population they serve so that playgroups become weekly boarding schools and toddlers are bussed from miles around.

The BMH's will be putting their 'Vacancies' signs outside. Soldiers unfortunate enough to be admitted to hospital are likely to be there for some time for all the consultants to do some work. He'll not go short of female attention. The nurses will be squabbling over who is going to do the injection and who's going to take his pulse. By the time he's been through the Fractures Clinic, Vasectomy Clinic and Open Heart Surgery he'll come out feeling like a new man.

Everyone will be sorry when the Brits leave Germany. The Germans more than most. The economy of places has practically depended upon soldiers' pay. German shopkeepers and barmen may once have despised the Brits, now they'll be dragging them into their shops and beer kellars claiming that, 'We speak English'...quite unheard of before. Perhaps if they started another war - would that make the Brits stay?

"Speaking as a daschund, I don't find the idea of staying behind so bad."

"BMH have got him Sir - he went in with eye trouble and piles, now he's circumcised and transferred to the surgical ward."

"You've got to help me Sir - they got me in for an eye test and now I'm excused boots for ten months."

"We also old cameraden - Regimental old comrades."

"Hans here says, would we like some schnapps - and before we leave could we do something environmentally unfriendly to the cobbles in his yard, for old times sake?"

"And the same to you mit schlag on it!"

Sell off or sell-out?

"Welcome to the Bad Breth Garrison Brownie economy pack."

NO MORE JOBS FOR THE BOYS

As you would expect the Forces are pretty regimented when it comes to redundancy and resettlement. On a given day once a year a letter will arrive to thousands of officers and men to inform them that their services will no longer be required. In this way, thousands of men trained in the arts of warfare, drinking and sleeping rough will appear on the job market together. It's a bit of a blow for officers and soldiers alike if they get chosen for redundancy when they didn't even apply. It doesn't help having those who are in safe jobs giving advice on what they would do with the money if they had got it.

For the line infantry, commandos, paras and the like, selling their skills should be easy enough if only they could find someone interested in employing men who can kill with one hand but want half the year off to go skiing and sailing. RAF Pilots should come off better on the job market once they remember that no-one actually flies aircraft anymore. Civilian pilots have left it to the auto-pilot for years. They don't get done for pilot error. Working in a civilian job will take some getting used to. But after a few weeks, even the slowest of VC10 pilots will have worked out that the seats face forwards and it's the toilet not the flight deck at the rear of a civvy aeroplane.

When you're trying to get a job in Civvy Street, remember the three basic 'Don'ts':

Don't call the man behind the desk 'Sir';

Don't stand up straight, chest out, chin up in front of the desk instead of taking a seat;

Don't salute as you enter the office.

"Either we're redundant or there's something wrong with the aircraft."

"Redundancy is a terrible thing Frobisher!"

"No Corporal, you can't stay on - not even as cannon fodder!"

"To save money this year Smurthwaite we've combined your annual Confidential Report and an Option for Change."

"I'm sorry Sir, it's quite clear - wine tasting for Cavalry, grape treading for Infantry."

"What we're going on with today gentlemen, is beating your swords into ploughshares."

"Doing a resettlement course - English as a foreign language - noch ein bier bitte landlord."

"Don't worry dear - Private Smudge in the stores assures me he'll fix me up with a suitable job."

"I think you ought to try and have a word with him darling, he's something big in Y-fronts."

"We're looking for a man like you to market our new, hi-tech, state of the art chastity belts to H.M. Forces on unaccompanied postings."

"That's ridiculous - the Army always said one leg was longer than the other, now you're telling me one leg is shorter!"

"Have you thought of trying the professional and executives register?"

"Something seems to be coming through on the old boy network."

"Frankly I don't believe that someone who has been an early warning system and a deterrent can suddenly become user friendly!"

"We're looking for a new scrum half on the Metropolitan Line next season Major."

"How about this? Old established circus requires sword swallower for matinees and evenings, full life cover included, owning own sword an advantage."

"We find these ex-service types make excellent high pressure salesmen."

"The thing you will find most difficult Barbour is remembering that you are no longer in uniform."

"He's looking for a nice nine to five security job somewhere in the Ipswich area."

"We're marketing a brand new swear word next year and we are looking for high expletive experts like you Sergeant Major to sell it for us."

"Flight Lieutenant Flash Gordon, recently of the RAF Red Arrows presents his compliments and suggests that you hang onto your drinks while we fly in formation with Flights 109 and 110 to Los Angeles at varying heights and speeds."

"Frankly Padre, I found your CV a touch holier than thou."

"And on my right - an unfrocked Padre late of Rheindahlen Garrison."

"It wasn't actually the Queens Birthday Parade you were watching it was the Brigade of Guards busking."

"Layout artist required at funeral parlour - no previous experience or arts degree necessary."

"In this work Vest you're an early warning system AND a deterrent."

"Hey Di - I've landed a job as a miner."

"So is 'No war' mate - so is NO war."

WHAT WILL BECOME OF THE VESTS AND THE BARBOURS?

Five years on from Options what will the Barbours and Vests have made of Civvy Street? Will they be faced with a future of camping holidays as Corporal Vest and Major Barbour yearn for the rugged outdoor life they had on exercise? Or will they have made it and done what the Army could never promise, got rich quick?

Major Barbour like many officers will bring certain skills and attributes to civilian life. As an officer he had a talent for leadership, avoiding taking instant decisions and conversation. Vital qualities indeed for someone commanding men, who wanted to avoid all controversial decisions and was capable of deflecting all flak over long boozy lunches in the officer's mess.

In civilian life his manner may easily be misunderstood as arrogant and insufferable. His adeptness at delegating all routine work interpreted as idleness. He never wanted to be a civilian. He'll call himself Major Barbour, wear his brown trilby and British Warm to his dying day.

Corporal Vest's army career has been the perfect preparation for civilian life. He lived by his wits, being invaluable to his CO in fixing all those delicate little jobs. As delegation went down the chain of command it stopped right there at Corporal Vest. He was Mr Fixit. It was on exercise that he came into his own. He specialised in fixing the impossible, procuring the unobtainable, of finding girls in Belfast and booze in Norway. If his CO had wanted penguin pie in the Falklands he'd have found it. Corporal Vest was always a most obliging sort.

The only difference Civvy Street will make to Corporal Vest is that he can do all the fixing for himself.

"Cor Mister Barbour - remember how the lads used to get soaked on exercises and you couldn't leave your command vehicle?"

"I've found a super pair of used wellies at the Oxfam shop with a guarentee of only 30 miles on the soles."

"All the other council tenants park their transport on the grass verge Officer - I park Henry."

"But darling - it's only the WI Christmas pantomime."

"Why do you need the b.......y Volvo to meet Mrs Barbour at the nearly new shop?"

"You remember Mrs Vest and Jason dear? - we've been getting Adrian his sports coat for his new school."

"Guess what Di - I've been invited to join the Old Boy network?"